Calendar 2000

		APRIL						
S	—	2	9	16	23	30		
M	—	3	10	17	24	—		
T	—	4	11	18	25	—		
W	—	5	12	19	26	—		
T	—	6	13	20	27	—		
F	—	7	14	21	28	—		
S	1	8	15	22	29	—		

		MAY					
S	—	7	14	21	28		
M	1	8	15	22	29		
T	2	9	16	23	30		
W	3	10	17	24	31		
T	4	11	18	25	—		
F	5	12	19	26	—		
S	6	13	20	27	—		

		JUNE				
S	—	4	11	18	25	
M	—	5	12	19	26	
T	—	6	13	20	27	
W	—	7	14	21	28	
T	1	8	15	22	29	
F	2	9	16	23	30	
S	3	10	17	24	—	

3

£5.70

WHAT A LOT

Rachel comes to a big decision on page 6.

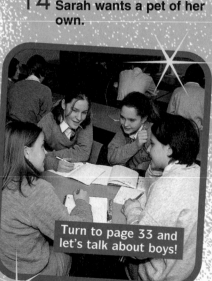

Turn to page 33 and let's talk about boys!

Panto girl Suzannah meets Ant and Dec. It's behind you on page 102!

Printed and Published in Great Britain by D.C. Thomson & Co. Ltd., 185 Fleet Street, London EC4A 2HS.
© D.C. Thomson & Co., Ltd., 1999 **ISBN** 0–85116–701–2

We've GoT!

Getting to know you on page 54.

What's Kelly searching for? Turn to page 120 to find out.

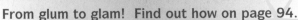

From glum to glam! Find out how on page 94.

A new bedroom? It's plain sailing for Hayley on page 124.

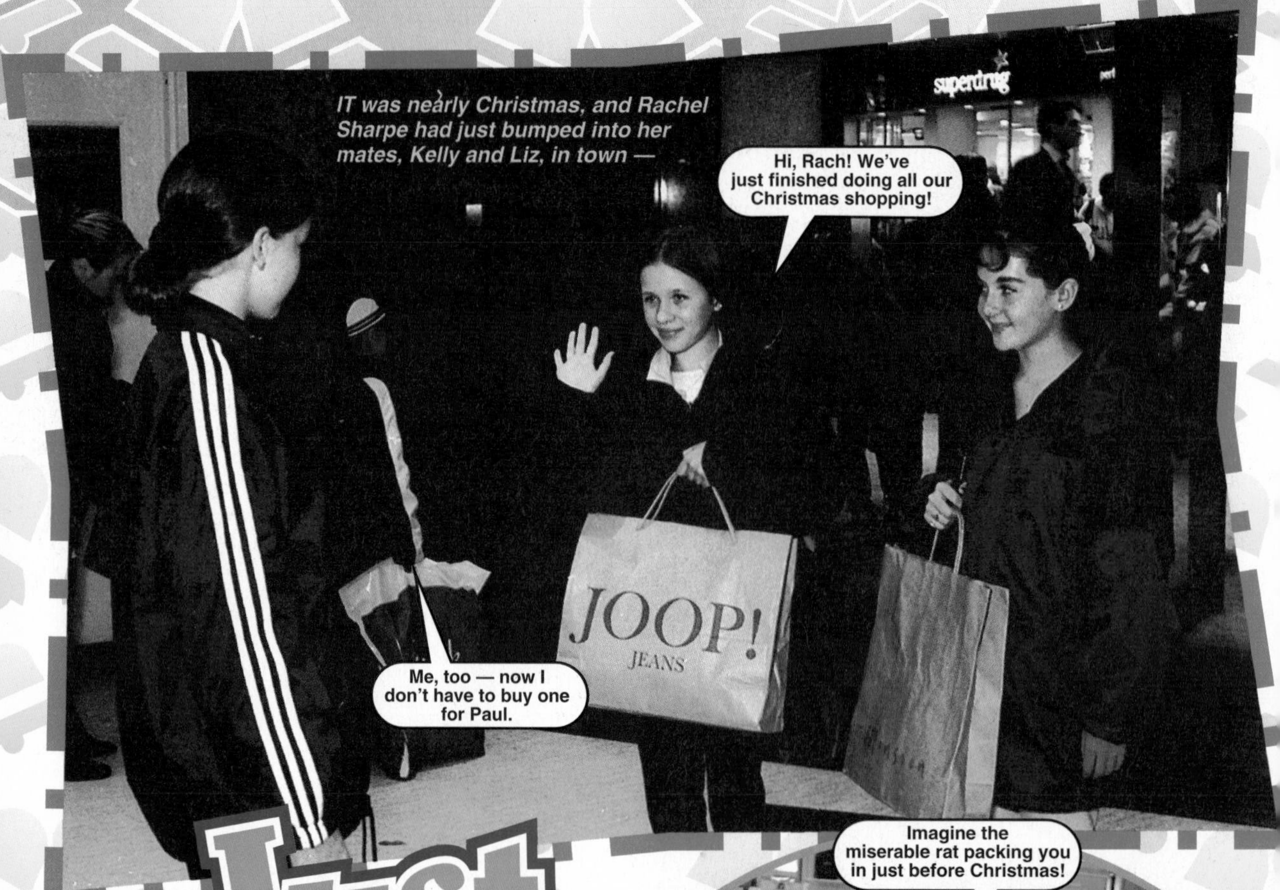

Just Good Friends

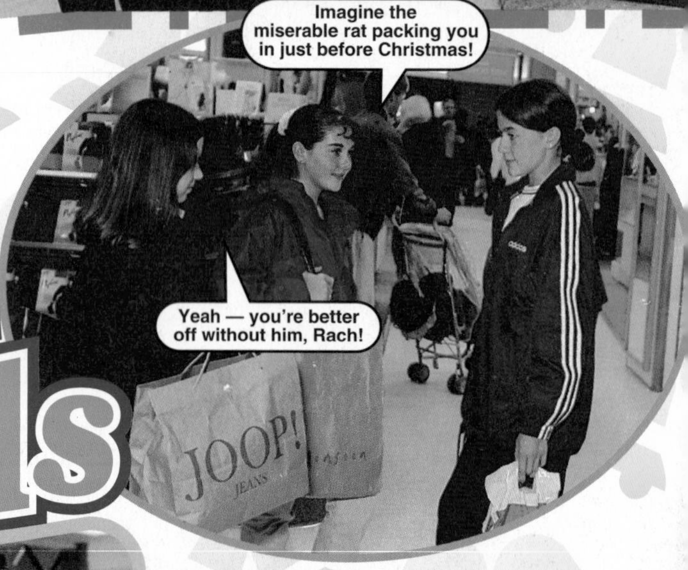

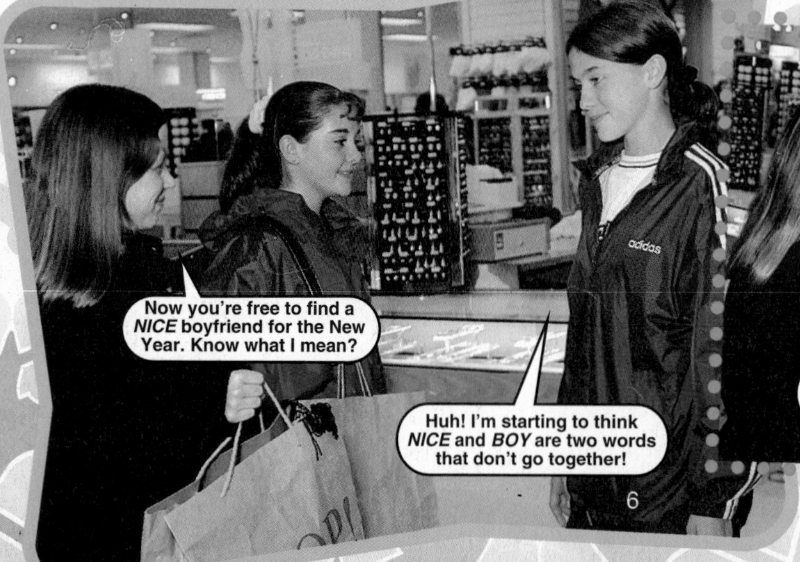

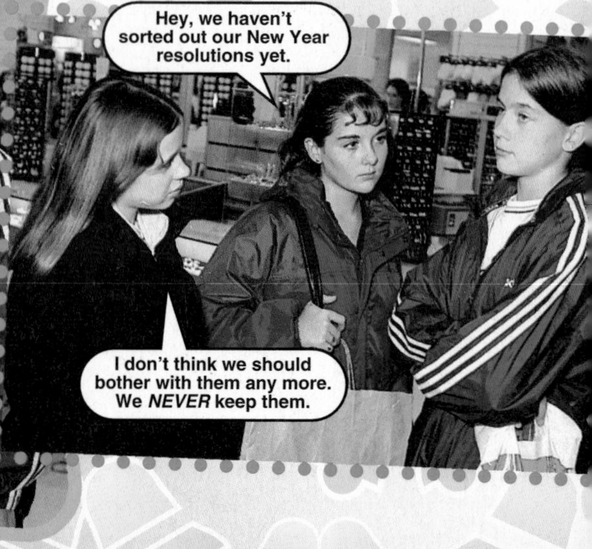

8

9

10

Victoria's secret talent is being able to do animal impressions.

Mel G writes poems about her feelings and emotions.

Mel C used to work in a chip shop!

Baby Spice loves America because she can go non-stop shopping!

Cleo hates mushy peas!

It takes Cleopatra's mum between six and eight hours to plait each girl's hair!

Vernie Bennett from Eternal's two fave things are Japan and baked beans!

Naima from The Honeyz conditions her hair with mayonnaise.

Yonah would love her sister, Zainam, to design a party outfit for her!

Shaznay spends two hours getting ready for a date.

All Saints' Mel can touch her nose with her tongue!

Cleopatra's Yonah loves munching pears!

Yonah irritates the other Cleopatra girls when she cracks her fingers.

Nicole has two fillings and takes two sugars in hot drinks.

You'll never see Cleopatra girls comin' atcha in the colour pink. They reckon it's too girlie for them!

Eternal's Kelle Bryan has three tattoos!

Cleo hates her feet — but doesn't know why!

The girls in Solid HarmoniE never bother giving each other make-overs as they have to wear make-up every day.

12

Girls! Girls! Girls!

Think you know all there is to know about your fave girl bands? Read on for even *more* fab facts and info!

Caroline Corr just loves to go paragliding!

Andrea Corr loves to spend Sundays catching up on EastEnders and drinking lots of tea.

Andrea's fave dish is baked cod with olives, olive oil and tomatoes.

Edele would like to have twins when she's older.

Sinead's fave TV programme is Blind Date!

Keavy once turned a bath purple with her hair dye!

Lyndsay lived in Greece until she was thirteen!

13

NO PETS ALLOWED!

"GOOD boy, Monty. Fetch the stick!"

Sarah loved playing with her friend, Clare's, young puppy. The two friends took Monty to the park every day. Monty ran eagerly for the stick, picked it up in his soft mouth and dropped it obediently at Sarah's feet. She rewarded him with a couple of chocolate drops.

"You're so patient with Monty," Clare remarked as the girls walked home for tea. "He's really taken to you. Did you ask your mum and dad about getting a puppy for your birthday?"

Sarah looked down at loveable Monty as he scampered along at her heels.

"There's no point," she said sadly. "We're not allowed pets in our new flat. It's the rules."

Sarah's family had had to move to this new area because of Dad's new job. She felt lucky that she had made such a nice friend as Clare but she hated having to leave her pets behind.

"Tell me about your pets again," said Clare as the girls turned the corner near where they lived.

"There was Jess our black cat," smiled Sarah. "He was a real softie and wanted to be cuddled all the time. Gran looks after him now. Then there was Bouncer, my tiny dwarf rabbit. She liked to hop all over the lawn looking for her favourite dandelion leaves. We gave her to our neighbour. I know they'll be well-cared for but I really miss them."

"Don't worry," said Clare kindly, "You can share Monty with me."

* * * * * *

That night in bed Sarah felt even more sad when she took out her photos of Jess and Bouncer. She remembered what Mum had said on the day they moved house.

"You'll have more time to play and make new friends without pets to look after," she'd said. "No more cleaning out, feeding and grooming." But that was just what Sarah liked. She loved caring for animals. That's why the teacher at her old school always chose Sarah to look after the school pets during the holidays.

"Have you decided on your birthday present yet, Sarah?" Dad asked at breakfast. "I know you'd like some money for clothes but I'd like to buy you a proper present too."

"All I want is a pet, Dad," said Sarah, looking glum.

"Oh, Sarah," Mum said, shaking her head. "You know it's not allowed. I'm afraid that's final."

* * * * * *

Sarah's birthday arrived. Her mum and dad gave her a clothes gift voucher, Clare bought her a pretty necklace and Monty 'handed over' a packet of his favourite chocolate drops!

Sarah had some lovely cards, too, but saved the extra-large white envelope till last. When she opened it she had a shock.

"It's a birthday card from Rosie," she said looking puzzled. "But I don't know anyone called Rosie!"

"You will very soon," grinned Dad.

Mum picked up the photograph of a beautiful brown-eyed donkey that had fallen from the card.

"It's from the sanctuary that cares for ill-treated and homeless donkeys," she explained. "It says thank you, Sarah, for adopting me. Please visit as often as you can. Love Rosie."

"So get your coat on, Sarah," said Dad. "We're going there now. It's only up the road."

Sarah was thrilled. Ten minutes later she was at the sanctuary where she and Rosie made friends straightaway. At last Sarah felt happy. Rosie was just what she wanted. A pet of her very own.

The End

14

nurses on t.v.

FRIENDS, Verity, Amanda, Jackie and Kay, were student nurses at Norchester General Hospital. One day, as Verity and Amanda began their shift —

WARDS 10-12 →

Hey, that's Carrie Carson — the TV presenter!

You're right, Verity! What's *SHE* doing here? She doesn't look ill.

She must be visiting someone. Just wait till we tell the others!

But, at lunchtime —

Guess who *WE* saw this morning?

Carrie Carson.

Aw, you know! How come?

'Cos *WE* saw her, too. She came on our ward.

Was she visiting somebody, Jackie?

No, just looking round.

15

A few days later —

Before I start today's lecture, I have some news. A TV documentary about hospital life is going to be filmed at the General.

So *THAT'S* why Carrie was here. She must be presenting it.

So we'll be TV stars?

Hardly. A few of you may feature when individual case histories are told, and some of your lessons with me may also be filmed, but that's all.

A few days later a television crew arrived —

Oh, I hope it's not me! I'm useless in the classroom!

Wow! They must be starting filming today.

CEEBE TV

Verity was on Accident and Emergency —

Over here, nurse! Quickly!

Here we have a most unusual case . . .

It feels really weird being filmed at work.

18

Doctor Barlow sent the TV crew to a different ward —

Oh! Where have they gone? Why aren't they filming me?

They're needed somewhere else. Now, I shall need to do a series of painful tests.

Don't bother! I feel *FINE* now.

You were making it up, weren't you? Acting up because the cameras were here.

All right, I admit it. But it's not every day a drama student gets the chance to be filmed by a top TV director. I wanted to be discovered!

Well, then, go to auditions! But don't come bothering *US* again—.

Good for Doctor Barlow! He soon put her in her place. Life's *ALWAYS* eventful at Norchester General, but I've a feeling it will be even worse with these TV cameras!

CONTINUED ON PAGE 97.

19

Horse Laughs

I LOVE A SNOWFALL. YOU CAN FOLLOW THE FOOTPRINT TRACKS — THIS ONE LOOKS LIKE A DEER.

SEE!

THESE PRINTS CAN ONLY BE —

A DUCK!

AND THESE ARE RABBIT PRINTS!

WHAT TRAIL ARE YOU FOLLOWING, SCAMP?

NEED YOU ASK? THE FOOD TRAIL, OF COURSE!

the bakers

Hey, Jen, let's go in there!

Too late, Rachel! Snooty Mrs Onions from next door has spotted us!

Tell your mother I'll be popping round to see her later as I need to ask her a favour. Oh, I say — Mrs Charnwood-Briggs . . .

SISTERS, Jenny and Rachel Baker, were shopping in town —

So —

Hello, Mrs Onions!

O'NIONS dear. My name is Mrs O'NIONS.

We MUST arrange dinner, my dear.

Thank goodness for Mrs Charnwood-Briggs. Old Onions likes to hob-nob with people like her. But I wonder why she wants MUM?

21

'We *MUST* arrange dinner, my dear.'

Yuk! Who'd want to have dinner with *THEM?*

That evening —

I want you to bake a cake for my fund raising sale. The mayoress will be attending, of course.

I think Mum's supposed to be impressed.

Now I don't want an *ORDINARY* sponge. You'll bake something special, won't you, dear, for such an important event?

I think I can manage that, Mrs O'Nions.

When Mrs Onions had gone —

What a cheek! Your *ORDINARY* sponges are lovely, Mum.

Never mind. I'll do something nice, with a fancy decoration to keep Mrs O'Nions happy . . .

On Saturday morning —

What are you making with that yukky papier maché, Rachel?

A mask. A big scary one.

We're ready for the eggs now, Jenny . . . oh, there's the phone.

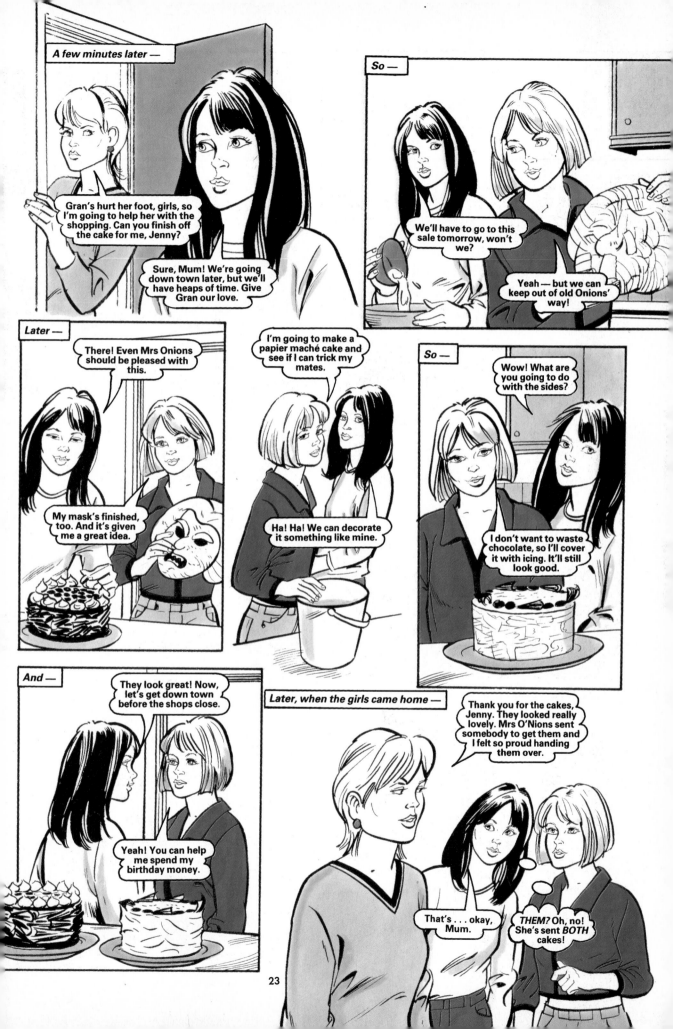

23

The papier maché cake's gone as well. We've got to get it back.

We'll go really early tomorrow and see if we can find it.

So —

Have you — er — sold a lot of cakes, then?

We certainly have! There were some LOVELY ones. They always sell quickly.

Oh, dear! I just hope whoever's bought it can take a joke.

Thank goodness Mrs Onions never collects things herself. At least she won't know WE'RE responsible. Uh-oh, here she comes!

Now, my dears, I need a little help and I'm SURE I can count on you.

Of COURSE, Mrs O'Nions.

Like we've got a choice!

Soon —

This is boring. Can't we make an excuse and leave, Jen?

I feel too guilty about the cake. We'll have to stay.

Later —

I've been so busy all day I've only just realised we got two papers this morning. One must belong to Mrs O'Nions. Take it round for me, girls.

Oh, no! I hope she hasn't found out about the cake.

24

THE END

best friend's boy

I'm really lucky having a mate like Emma. Some girls can be really nasty when their best friends have boyfriends, but Emma never minds me going out with Andy.

Later —

Andy's dead nice, too. He never makes a fuss if I want to go out with Emma.

Next day, at Emma's house —

We're going to Gran's for tea tonight and we'll probably stay late. I'll see you tomorrow at the sports centre, Nat.

Okay! See you then. 'Bye, Emma!

Natalie, can you just answer that phone for me, dear? I'll be there in a minute.

Sure, Mrs Ryan.

Hello! Is that Emma?

Er — no! Hang on!

It's someone for Emma.

Thanks, Natalie. I'll take it now.

Weird! It was a boy on the phone and he sounded just like Andy. But it can't have been. Why would he want to ring Emma?

Later, at home —

I'm really sorry, Nat, but I've got a load of homework to finish. I'm going to have to cancel tonight.

Okay, Andy. Don't worry about it. I've an essay to write, so I'll get on with that instead.

Odd! Andy's never stayed in to do homework on a Saturday. And Emma said she'd be busy, too. WAS it Andy on the phone at Emma's house? Can there be something going on between them?

No, I'm just being stupid! Andy and Emma would never cheat on me — they're my MATES!

Next day —

Did you have a good time at your gran's, Emma?

Yeah! My cousins were there as well, though. We came home early, 'cos Mum had a headache.

Oh! So Emma WAS home in the evening. Maybe she knew she'd be back early and she arranged to meet Andy, then he made an excuse not to see me.

I hope the pool's not crowded. I want to have a good swim today. What about you, Nat?

Er — yeah. Sure.

Tch! This is silly. I trust Emma. She's my best friend. I KNOW she wouldn't two-time me.

29

Later, at Andy's house —

Did you get all your homework done yesterday?

What? Um — yes! Well — not all of it. I'll finish it later. D'you want a Coke?

Andy was really shifty just now when I asked about his work. *COULD* he have been with Emma last night?

Back at home —

I don't know what to think any more! I know they're my friends, but still . . .

It's no good! I'll *HAVE* to find out if they're cheating on me. I can't say anything to them until I know for sure what's going on, so I'll just watch and see if I can catch them out.

Next day —

Coming round tonight, Nat?

Sorry, I can't! Mum's been nagging me to tidy my room. I'd better do it tonight.

Good. Now Emma's not expecting me, I can call round later. If Andy's there I'll know for sure.

So —

Hi, Emma! I finished early so I thought I'd come round after all.

Great! Come in then.

30

I'll get some drinks. You go on upstairs, Nat.

Okay.

Well, Andy's not here, that's for sure. Oh! What's that in the bin?

Prawn Cocktail flavour! That's Andy's favourite. What if he's been here already?

Next day, after school —

So the lab was flooded and we got off Science. It was a great laugh!

Wow! Some folk have all the luck!

Tch! Andy keeps talking to Emma. He *MUST* fancy her! I'll check up tonight. If Emma *AND* Andy are out, then I bet they're meeting one another.

So, later —

That's it! Emma and Andy told me they'd be staying in tonight, but they're *BOTH* out.

They *MUST* be seeing each other. I bet Andy's planning to dump me. Well, I won't give him the chance!

And, next morning —

Hey, Nat — listen to this! Me and Andy have something to tell you.

Huh! Have you? Well, you don't need to bother! I know already.

What do you mean, you know already?

31

Tch! You two must think I'm thick! Did you think I wouldn't realise you've been seeing each other behind my back?

WHAT? You're kidding, Nat! Of course we haven't been dating.

What makes you think that? I was only going to say that Andy has fixed me up with one of his mates for the school disco. We can go as a foursome.

But you've both been out at the same time.

Yeah, meeting up with Mike. Andy's never asked me out, Nat. And anyway, I wouldn't date my best friend's boy.

Oh, I've been really stupid, imagining all sorts. I'm so sorry. How can I ever make it up to you?

Just tell me you'll come to the disco with me and have a great time.

Of course I'll come. I can't think of anything I'd like more than going out with my *TWO* best friends. We'll *ALL* have a great time!

THE END

32

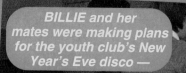

BILLIE and her mates were making plans for the youth club's New Year's Eve disco —

I know we've always gone to the disco as a gang, but how about finding partners this year?

Brilliant idea, Billie!

Yeah! We always miss out on the New Year's kisses, but we won't this year!

THE BoY FoR BiLLiE

But, after school —

It seemed a good idea at the time but who'll I ask? Maybe Lee Starkey in our class — he's dead nice.

Next day —

Lee Starkey's asked me to the disco!

I'm going with Mike Adams.

Paul's asked me and Nat's going with Rick.

35

Meet JO 'EUREKA' JOHNSON — RESIDENT CLEVER-CLOGS!

YUK! EVERY TIME I TRY TO GIVE BARKER A BATH, *I* END UP THE WETTEST! WHAT HE NEEDS IS A BATHING MACHINE!

One of Eureka's brilliant ideas is brewing!

IDEAS

EUREKA!

Soon —

THERE! THE HOSE IS READY AND THE TRAP'S SET. NOW TO LAY THE BAIT AND MAKE MYSELF SCARCE.

But, before she could hide —

BAH! BARKER'S MANAGED TO GET THE CHOCS *OUT* OF THE TRAP!

Then —

UH-OH! IT'S DAD.

TCH! SOMEONE COULD TRIP OVER THIS ROPE!

FUNNY — IT SEEMS TO BE CAUGHT ON SOMETHING!

It was — the tap!

GLUBB! PTOO!

CRIKEY! DAD'S TAKING A SHOWER AND IT'S NOT A FRIDAY NIGHT!

Another idea later —

PUFF, PANT! NOW TO COVER IT WITH LEAVES.

LET'S SEE BARKER GET OUT OF *THIS* ONE!

Soon —

ROWWR! RURRGH!

39

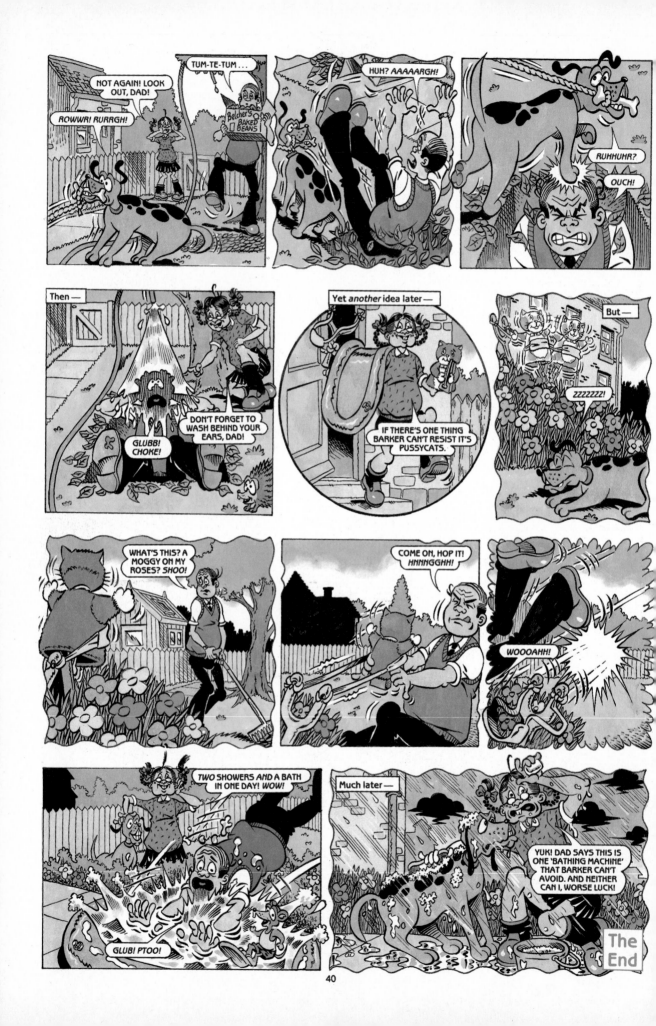

40

christmas past

IT was Christmas Eve and everyone, except Alison, was looking forward to all the fun and excitement of Christmas Day.

Huh! Christmas presents look good until you open them, then it's always a *BIG* disappointment!

43

44

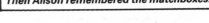

I didn't sell any matches today, so it's broth and bread for us for Christmas. I'd hoped to be able to buy Ben a little treat.

Broth and bread! Is that all they have? We eat till we burst on Christmas Day!

Mam's poorly, so it's up to me to look after her and Ben.

They've hardly anything and yet they're sharing what they have with me. I feel dead ashamed. I wish I could help in some way.

Later —

It's getting dark. I'll walk you back to the market square.

Here, Ben! Have these as a Christmas present from me.

Cor, thank you! I look a real toff, don't I, Mam?

Happy Christmas!

It WILL be a happy Christmas for Lizzie and her family. I've left my silver cat charm on Lizzie's tray. That should pay for a good dinner for them.

46

47

48

MAKE 'N' DO

This cute clown cake is dead easy and fun to make. It's great for parties or you could even give it to a mate for a birthday prez!

WHAT YOU NEED:

For the cake:
1 packet of sponge sandwich cake mix
1 egg
Water
Jam (choose your fave flavour)

For the decoration:
1 pack of white ready to roll icing
Foam bananas
Maltesers
Giant foam strawberry or marshmallow
Red food colouring
Blue, yellow or green food colouring

* We bought all our sweets from a pick 'n' mix counter to save buying a whole packet of each kind.

WHAT TO DO:

1. Follow the directions on the cake mix pack and make 2 sponge cakes.

2. When they're cool, sandwich them together with the jam. If they've risen a lot and there's a big bump in the middle, ask an adult to cut a bit off to leave a nice flat surface.

3. Now for the decoration. Before you start to roll out the icing, cut a small piece (about 2cm wide) off the end and put it aside. Follow the instructions on the pack and roll out the icing till it's big enough to cover your cake.

4. Spread a thin layer of jam all over the cake to help the icing stick. Put the icing on to the cake and gently smooth over the edges. Don't worry about bumps on the sides, the Clown's ruffle will cover them.

5. Start to make the face —
eyes: Maltesers or jelly beans.
hair: foam bananas.
nose: foam strawberry or marshmallow.

6. For the hat and the mouth, cut your little piece of icing in half. Add a few drops of red colour to one piece and knead the icing until it turns red. Roll out and cut a mouth shape. Use a little dab of water to stick it on the cake.

Make the hat in the same way, but use a different colour.

* This last bit is messy but fun, but if you're in a rush you can buy ready coloured Ready to Roll icing. One pack usually contains 4 or 5 different colours.

FOR THE NECK RUFFLE:

You'll need a pack of crepe paper and a glue stick.

1. When you take the paper out of the pack, leave it folded. Cut 2 strips around 3cm wide off the end.

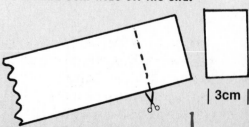

| 3cm |

1

stick

2

2. Unfold the strips and stick two ends together at right angles.

3. Now start to fold one strip over the other. Keep folding the paper over and over till you come to the end of the strips. You should have a square of folded paper — like a concertina. Stick the two strips together. Trim off any little extra bits.

3

4. Gently pull out the ruffle and wrap it round your cake. Stick the 2 ends together.

4

* Remember — always ask an adult before using any kitchen equipment.

FILM FUN

Find out if you're a film star fan or a film star flop in this all-star game of true or false. Give yourself one point for every correct answer.

Leonardo DiCaprio
★ Leo's top film Titanic lasted a massive three hours and 14 mins.
★ His parents are called George and Irmelin.
★ Leo will be 25 on November 11 in the year 2000.

Gwyneth Paltrow
★ Gwyneth's Oscar winning film Shakespeare in Love was written by William Shakespeare.
★ In Steven Spielberg's Hook, Gwyneth played a young Wendy.
★ Gwyneth is fluent in Spanish and French.

Robin Williams
★ Robin was the voice of the genie in the film Aladdin.
★ Patch Adams was based on a true story.
★ He played an Irish housekeeper in Mrs Doubtfire.

Will Smith
★ Will starred in the film Men in Black Suits.
★ He's so good at golf he could be the next Tiger Woods.
★ Will's a top pop singer as well as an actor.

Claire Danes
★ Claire is a student at posh Yale University in America.
★ She starred in the big screen version of Les Miserables.
★ Dressed as a boy, she played Romeo in Romeo and Juliet.

Brad Pitt
★ Brad was once engaged to Gwyneth Paltrow.
★ He was a choirboy in his hometown of Springfield, Missouri.
★ Seeing John Travolta in Saturday Night Fever made him want to be an actor.

Matt Le Blanc
★ He played Don East in Lost in Space.
★ Matt was a former Levi's 501 jeans model.
★ Friends co-star Jennifer Aniston was once his fiancée.

Kate Winslet
★ Kate's character in Titanic was called Poppy.
★ She had bangers and mash at her wedding reception.
★ Kate played Emma Thompson's sister in Jane Austen's Sense and Sensibility.

Jim Carrey
★ Jim and Mariah Carey are brother and sister.
★ Ace Ventura: Pet Detective was set in Africa.
★ Jim was the star of The Mask of Zorro.

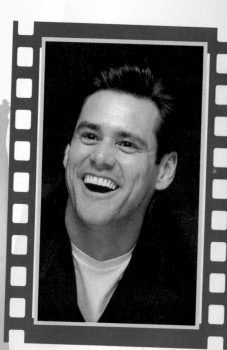

Answers

Jim: 1-False. 2-False (America). 3-False (The Mask).

Kate: 1-False (Rose). 2-True. 3-True.

Matt: 1-False (Don West). 2-True. 3-False.

Brad: 1-True. 2-True. 3-True.

Claire: 1-True. 2-True. 3-False (she was Juliet).

Will: 1-False (Men in Black). 2-True. 3-True.

Robin: 1-True. 2-True. 3-False (Scottish).

Gwyneth: 1-False (Tom Stoppard). 2-True. 3-True.

Leo: 1-True. 2-True. 3-False (26).

Scores

1-9: Not so good. You're the fall guy of the movies.
10-18: Very good. You're understudy to the stars.
19-27: You're the star! Have an Oscar!

Welcome to the farm!

OPEN TUE–SUN ~ 8·30–5pm

Admission is free, but we welcome donations...

We have a few 'Don'ts' ~ these are:
no smoking in farm buildings
no dogs
no children under 8 without a responsible adult
no handling or feeding animals without asking

We hope you enjoy your visit ~
feel free to ask questions...!

~ Farm shop & café open weekends + holidays ~

Visiting a farm used to mean a trip to the countryside, but not any more! Many places have their own City Farm and Katie and Sarah would like to show you round theirs.

DOWN ON THE FARM

The donkeys are always happy to see visitors — they're hoping you've brought them something to eat!

Because the animals are used to children being around them, they're all very tame and enjoy being petted — especially the goats.

Being cared for inside are some of the baby animals, like this cute kid. If you're lucky, you can even help to give them their bottles!

Keeping extra warm are these tiny chicks. They'll stay in their incubator until they're strong enough to go outside.

We're piggy mad, so we just love these little piglets. They wouldn't stay still for a moment, and kept making funny squeaking noises!

Some of the animals have been rescued and some have been brought in by people who can't look after them, like this cuddly rabbit.

The volunteers take great care of the animals and even the ones who live outside, like this cow and her lovely, white calf, are brought in for the night.

It's time to say goodbye, but Katie and Sarah won't get very far hitching a ride on this pig — it's a wooden carving!

YOUR

ARIES (Mar 21-Apr 20)

USUALLY YOU'RE — ready to try anything and bursting with confidence! Enthusiastic about starting things, you're always impatient to finish them. Loud on the outside, you're quiet on the inside.

THIS YEAR YOU'RE — calmer and more careful about things you do. Full of interesting ideas, you'll still be keen to listen to others.

TRY TO — share more.

TRY NOT TO — speak without stopping to think.

GOOD MONTHS — April, August, September.

NOT SO GOOD MONTHS — February, May, October.

GEMINI (May 21-June 21)

USUALLY YOU'RE — happy to let everyone around you work hard and get things done. Quite artistic, you're a good performer when you *have* to be, but when you *don't*, you can be a bit lazy.

THIS YEAR YOU'RE — going to have to get used to being busier! You'll have the chance to join in a lot of different groups and events.

TRY TO — organise your room!

TRY NOT TO — let other people make decisions for you.

GOOD MONTHS — January, June, November.

NOT SO GOOD MONTHS — April, August, December..

LEO (July 24-Aug 23)

USUALLY YOU'RE — always right. You hate to be proved wrong, and will work hard to make sure that's not the case. You're generous, caring and full of fun. You also like being the centre of attention.

THIS YEAR YOU'RE — busier than ever! You'll want to take part in lots of events in and out of school. At home, you need to be more tidy.

TRY TO — slow down a *little* bit.

TRY NOT TO — agree to do too many things.

GOOD MONTHS — January, April, July.

NOT SO GOOD MONTHS — March, August, November.

TAURUS (Apr 21-May 20)

USUALLY YOU'RE — pottering along doing what has to be done, never getting too excited or too upset. You're caring and sharing with a small circle of very good friends you should know for ever.

THIS YEAR YOU'RE — a lot more lively! New people will make you look at things in a new way. You may make a change in your appearance.

TRY TO — stand up for yourself more.

TRY NOT TO — agree to everything you're asked.

GOOD MONTHS — May, August, December.

NOT SO GOOD MONTHS — March, June, October.

CANCER (June 22-July 23)

USUALLY YOU'RE — found quietly reading or listening to music in your room. You can be a bit of a loner, but have plenty of interests and friends to keep you busy. You're also clever and kind but sometimes impatient.

THIS YEAR YOU'RE — happy to be part of some kind of team, and spending less time on your own. You may have to work hard at school.

TRY TO — do something different.

TRY NOT TO — believe *all* the gossip you hear.

GOOD MONTHS — February, May, September.

NOT SO GOOD MONTHS — April, July, October.

VIRGO (Aug 24-Sept 23)

USUALLY YOU'RE — hardworking and helpful, especially at home or in school. But you're popular with your friends too, being someone on whom they can rely. You always know what you want.

THIS YEAR YOU'RE — a little indecisive, but others will help you out if you ask them. You'll be impatient to finish something you start.

TRY TO — learn to take time out and relax.

TRY NOT TO — be too bossy with friends.

GOOD MONTHS — February, June, September.

NOT SO GOOD MONTHS — January, July, November.

YEAR!

BRA (Sept 24-Oct 23)

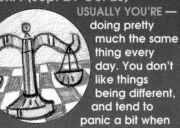

USUALLY YOU'RE — doing pretty much the same thing every day. You don't like things being different, and tend to panic a bit when ...ced with new things and faces. ...u're thoughtful and quiet.
...IS YEAR YOU'RE — facing quite a ...w changes and enjoying it. A few ...ew faces will soon become very ...od friends.
...Y TO — open up more with pals.
...Y NOT TO — refuse to try new ...ings.
...OD MONTHS — March, May, ...ugust.
...OT SO GOOD MONTHS — July, ...ptember, October.

...CORPIO (Oct 24-Nov 22)

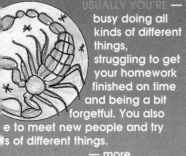

USUALLY YOU'RE — busy doing all kinds of different things, struggling to get your homework finished on time and being a bit forgetful. You also ...e to meet new people and try ...s of different things.
... — more ...ganised. You're also keen to ...ep your new year resolution and ...t spend all your pocket money ...one go.
...Y TO — save up for special ...ings.
...Y NOT TO — forget important ...ople and dates.
...OOD MONTHS — January, July, ...ovember.
...OT SO GOOD MONTHS — March, ...ne, September.

SAGITTARIUS (Nov 23-Dec 22)

USUALLY YOU'RE — involved in something arty or musical, being an expressive soul. You have lots of hobbies and lots of different friends. You can be argumentative, hating to be proved wrong.
THIS YEAR YOU'RE — surprised to discover a hidden talent. You may also find yourself given the chance to travel later in the year.
TRY TO — think before you speak.
TRY NOT TO — agree to join too many clubs.
GOOD MONTHS — February, September, December.
NOT SO GOOD MONTHS — April, July, October.

CAPRICORN (Dec 23-Jan 20)

USUALLY YOU'RE — arguing with someone because you're convinced you're right, or standing up for your friends. You're very protective of people you like and can be quite a bad enemy.
... — much less stubborn and keen to take up a new kind of sport or hobby. You're in great demand for some school project.
TRY TO — listen more carefully to close friends.
TRY NOT TO — interrupt or criticise people.
GOOD MONTHS — April, August, October.
NOT SO GOOD MONTHS — February, May, July.

AQUARIUS (Jan 21-Feb 19)

USUALLY YOU'RE — extremely organised and prepared for anything! You hate being late or made to wait for things and can be annoyed by forgetful friends. You love music and clothes.
THIS YEAR YOU'RE — much more patient and easy-going. You should get the chance to take part in something very exciting at school.
TRY TO — chat less on the phone.
TRY NOT TO — worry so much.
GOOD MONTHS — May, August, November.
NOT SO GOOD MONTHS — February, April, December.

PISCES (Feb 20-Mar 20)

USUALLY YOU'RE — wandering around in a world of your own, being kind to the environment, people and animals. You can be hard to track down because you're involved in so many things.
THIS YEAR YOU'RE — doing much the same as usual, adding even more to your long list of hobbies. You'll read and write even more than usual.
TRY TO — watch less television during the weekend!
TRY NOT TO — forget too many important dates.
GOOD MONTHS — June, September, December.
NOT SO GOOD MONTHS — March, August, October.

Seeing Stars!

Faye was excited — maybe he'd changed his mind and there was a part for her after all!

"ARE you going to audition for the school play?" Sita asked her mates, Faye and Polly, as they read the notice on the school board.

"You bet," said Faye. "I'd love to be on stage!"

So, after school on Friday, Sita, Faye and Polly made their way to the school hall where lots of girls had already gathered for the audition.

Mr Brown, the Drama teacher, explained that he had written a play with an Outer Space theme. Then he gave everyone some lines to read aloud. The audition took a long time, so while she was waiting, Faye took out her Art pad and felt pens and drew some space monsters and aliens.

Afterwards, Mr Brown called everyone together.

"Polly and Sita, I'd like you to have the leading roles."

The girls were delighted.

Then Mr Brown read out the rest of the cast — Faye's name wasn't mentioned. She was terribly disappointed. Sita and Polly felt sorry for their mate and didn't know what to say. They were glad when Mr Brown came over and asked Faye if she would like to help with the costumes.

"The backstage helpers are just as important as the actors," he told her.

Faye wasn't that keen, but murmured, "Okay."

"Never mind, love," Mum said at tea-time. "No-one can be good at everything. Don't forget, you always get top marks for Art. Anyway, I'm sure you'll enjoy helping with the costumes."

*   *   *   *

On Monday, at break, Mr Brown sent for Faye. Faye was excited — maybe he'd changed his mind and there *was* a part for her after all.

But Mr Brown looked quite serious.

"Faye, would you be very disappointed if I said I didn't want you to help with the costumes?" he asked.

Disappointed! Faye was devastated! It seemed that there was no place for her in the play at all.

"Only," Mr Brown continued, "I found these sketches in the hall on Friday after you had left. Are they yours?"

"Yes," whispered Faye, thinking he was now going to tell her off for leaving rubbish behind.

"Well," smiled Mr Brown. "These drawings are excellent — just the sort of thing we need for the backcloth. I'd really like you to paint the scenery."

Faye was over the moon with excitement.

"When can I start?" she grinned.

So, over the next few weeks, Faye designed and painted the backcloth at the back of the stage. Sita and Polly helped too when they weren't needed for rehearsals. In return, Faye helped her mates learn their lines.

When completed, the scenery looked stunning. Faye had designed a planet full of bizarre monsters and out-of-this-world landscapes.

A photograph of a scene from the play was featured in the local newspaper.

And, if you looked very carefully at the edge of the picture, you might just have noticed Faye's hand gripping a paintbrush as she put a few finishing touches to her masterpiece.

So Faye managed to appear on stage after all!

The End

time to talk

RACHEL MILLER and Julia Wade were best mates. One day, after school —

I'm meeting my mum from work today, Julia. Fancy a lift home?

That'd be brilliant, Rach. It's freezing today!

Rachel's mum had her very own talk show, Dr Frances, on the local radio.

You must be proud of your mum. Her show's dead popular. EVERYONE listens to it.

Yeah, it wasn't easy for her when Dad left.

Maybe that's why she's so understanding to all those people who phone in with their problems.

I'm just helping Sam make some Christmas cards.

Julia may envy me, but *I* envy *HER*, having a mum who gets involved in what her kids are doing.

I know my mum loves me, but she's so busy helping other people that *WE* never have any time together to sit and talk.

Julia's sister's given me an idea. I'll ask Mum to help *ME* make cards!

So next day, at Rachel's —

I'm going to make Christmas cards instead of buying them. Have you got any ideas for the design, Mum.

HUH? Er — sorry, Rachel. I was never any good at Art.

I was better at Drama and that sort of thing.

Well, I'm in the school play. Pity I already know my lines or I could've got Mum to help me with them. Still, she doesn't know that, does she?

And so, next day —

Mum, could you go through my lines for my part in the school play?

Sorry, love, I've got to go to the studio for a meeting about my special Christmas show.

Sorry, dear. I'm tired. But you've got to remember about all those poor unfortunate people out there.

Hang on, I've just thought of something!

So, on the evening of Mum's show —

. . . and now we have a special Christmas edition of *DR FRANCES* . . .

. . . so you must spend only what you can afford, Louise.

Mum's really good at giving advice —

In the radio studio —

ON AIR

Now we have 13-year-old Helen. And your problem is with your mother. Is that right, Helen?

Yes. She's always *BUSY* and I never see her. We never have time to talk.

I miss the things we used to do together.

I feel mean tricking Mum by using a false name, but how else could I get her to hear my problem?

You're right. Your mother *SHOULD* spend more time with you, Rachel — sorry, I mean Helen.

Mum *KNOWS* it's me!

63

If she's at work now, why don't you go and meet her?

Yes, I will. Thanks!

Soon—

Mum's waiting for me! Usually she's NEVER ready!

Hi, Rachel, or should I say Helen?

RECEPT

Sorry, Mum. I didn't mean to trick you.

I'm glad you did. I didn't realise how much I'd been neglecting you!

Now, let's get home to our lovely decorated house and make plans for the holiday.

HARDWARE

XMAS TREES

OPEN

♪We wish you a ♪ merry Christmas . . .

It IS going to be a merry Christmas now that I've got Mum back!

PUTERS TOYS AMES BIES

THE END

penny's place

PENNY JORDAN'S parents ran Penny's Place café in Chesterford. It was nearly Christmas and Penny had one more present to buy.

All I need is something for Donna's little sister, Kylie. I'll try here.

These dolls are nice — and they're not too expensive. I'm sure Kylie would love . . .

Hi! Can I help you?

Oh! Er — well —

Are you looking for something special?

Wow! HE'S certainly something special!

66

69

Horse Laughs

LOOK! THEY'RE PUTTING UP A FUN FAIR! MIND YOU, IT'S HARD WORK.

WISH I WAS WITH A FUNFAIR. I'D LOVE THAT LIFE.

WHAT!?! YOU HATE HARD WORK! YOU'RE FAR TOO LAZY TO WORK IN A FUNFAIR.

IF I WAS IN THE FUNFAIR I'D GALLOP AROUND ALL DAY.

OH, YEAH?

YEAH, I WOULD! THERE'S JUST ONE THING. I'D HAVE TO BE PAINTED BLUE WITH WHITE SPOTS.

NOW YOU'VE GONE COMPLETELY LOOPY!

NO . . . I'D BE JUST LIKE THEM.

I COULD GO FOR MILES AND I WOULDN'T HAVE TO MOVE A MUSCLE.

GROAN! TRUST SCAMP!

b*witched

westlife

boys! bo

Brill bits and pieces of essenti

A fan once tried to give Five a live toad in a crisp packet!

Abs hates flying insects. Rich hates spiders!

The film 'Watership Down' makes Spike from 911 cry!

Brian Backstreet would like to be Nick Backstreet for a day to find out what he's like as a friend!

Rich likes to stay in bed as long as possible on days off work!

Abs passed his driving test first time!

Backstreet Boy Brian was once fooled by someone who asked him to go and buy some tartan paint!

Nick BSB loves playing tricks on little bruv, Aaron Carter!

AJ drives the others crazy when he moans about having a bad hair day!

Backstreet Boys are addicted to M&Ms!

s! boys!

nfo on your fave boy bands!

Isaac Hanson's fave foods are nachos and popcorn!

Taylor Hanson couldn't live without a pen — for signing heaps of autographs!

Jimmy fancies Monica from Friends'!

Baby Spice is the most famous person in Lee's address book!

All the Hanson boys get into trouble at home if they don't do their chores!

Hanson have to study on tour because their parents are their tutors!

Ronan Keating was thrown out of his school choir for not being able to sing!

Boyzone's Ronan and Shane used to share a flat with Louise!

Mikey Graham's heroes are Sting and Al Pacino!

Shane Lynch's fave TV programme is Top Gear — he used to be a mechanic!

77

screen test!

Are you a telly addict?
Find out with our TV test!

cute couples!

Match up characters in the first column with their other halves in the second column.

VIC	MUTTLEY
WALLACE	KEL
DASTARDLY	HOMER
JULIA JEKYLL	GROMMIT
KIENAN	BOB
MARGE	HARRIET HYDE

in the box!

Find these fab TV programmes reading up, down, backwards, forwards or diagonally in our cool wordsearch:

BROOKSIDE, BYKER GROVE, BOY MEETS WORLD, CBBC, CORONATION STREET, DAWSON'S CREEK, EASTENDERS, FRIENDS, GRANGE HILL, HOME AND AWAY, HOLLYOAKS, NEWSROUND, PARTY OF FIVE, SM TV LIVE, THE O ZONE, TOP OF THE POPS, USA HIGH.

words! words! words!

How many words of three letters or more can you make from the letters in these words?

VAMPIRE SLAYER

Scores
35–40 Good 41–50 Very Good 51+ Excellent

T	A	B	D	L	R	O	W	S	T	E	E	M	Y	O
P	E	H	G	S	T	R	D	Z	E	F	D	C	D	E
A	C	E	I	Y	A	U	J	I	G	A	Y	P	F	G
R	D	N	R	B	C	W	H	K	W	Z	L	Q	E	I
T	E	O	J	T	X	V	L	S	N	A	N	R	V	L
Y	F	Z	K	L	S	M	O	O	B	M	O	S	O	N
O	H	O	M	E	A	N	D	A	W	A	Y	K	R	O
F	M	E	P	Q	S	P	O	G	J	K	S	A	G	K
F	N	H	F	C	T	E	D	I	S	K	O	O	R	B
I	O	T	R	U	S	R	Q	H	T	T	V	Y	E	D
V	W	E	I	A	B	E	F	I	U	A	W	L	K	C
E	E	X	E	V	I	L	V	T	M	S	N	L	Y	E
K	G	V	N	E	W	S	R	O	U	N	D	O	B	B
H	I	J	D	C	D	U	S	A	H	I	G	H	R	A
K	E	A	S	T	E	N	D	E	R	S	X	Y	Z	O
S	P	O	P	E	H	T	F	O	P	O	T	C	B	B

78

true or false

1. Friends' Jennifer Aniston once had a sculpture displayed in the New York Metropolitan Museum of Art.
2. Dawson's nickname, Oompa Loompa, in Dawson's Creek comes from the book "James and the Giant Peach" by Roald Dahl.
3. Declan Donnelly fancies Sabrina The Teenage Witch.
4. Episodes of SM:tv Live are only planned two weeks in advance.
5. Britney Spears appears in a few episodes of Hollyoaks.

planet pop!

Answer these questions and you'll find that the last letter of each answer is the first letter of the next answer in our great pop swirl!

1. A song may be this if it's not a miss or a maybe. (3)
2. BBC 1's top pop programme. (3,2,3,4)
3. In this programme people turn into pop stars. (5,2,5,4)
4. Top of the Pops 2 is shown on this day. (8)

quick quiz!

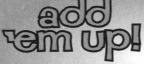

1. In which month did Adam Rickitt leave Coronation Street?
2. For how many years has Grange Hill been running?
3. Can you name the TV show presented by Ronan Keating?
4. Which instrument does Jesse Spencer like to play?
5. What unusual talent does Salem from Sabrina The Teenage Witch possess?

oap muddles!

Unravel these [le]tters to reveal six top TV soaps!

OTNANIRO TESTER

SADSTEEREN

SOBROIDEK

MEOH NAD WAAY

SOBRUNIGEH

SHOALKLOY

add 'em up!

Does CAT, ANT or DEC appear most in our small SM: tv Live wordsearch?

D	E	C	N	N
N	C	E	D	T
A	A	A	N	N
N	T	A	T	A
T	A	C	E	D

ANSWERS

PLANET POP!
1. Hit. 2. Top of the Pops. 3. Stars in Their Eyes. 4. Saturday.

QUICK QUIZ!
1. April. 2. 211 3. Get Your Act Together. 4. Violin. 5. Being able to speak.

SOAP MUDDLES!
Coronation Street, EastEnders, Brookside, Home and Away, Neighbours, Hollyoaks.

ADD 'EM UP!
They all appear three times.

TRUE OR FALSE
1. False. It was a painting. 2. False. It was Dawson's Creek.

CUTE COUPLES!
Kienan and kel, Charlie and the Chocolate Factory. 3. True. 4. True. 5. False. She appears in Homer.

Marge and Homer.
Vic and Bob, Wallace and Grommit, Dastardly and Muttley, Julia Jekyll and Harriet Hyde.

79

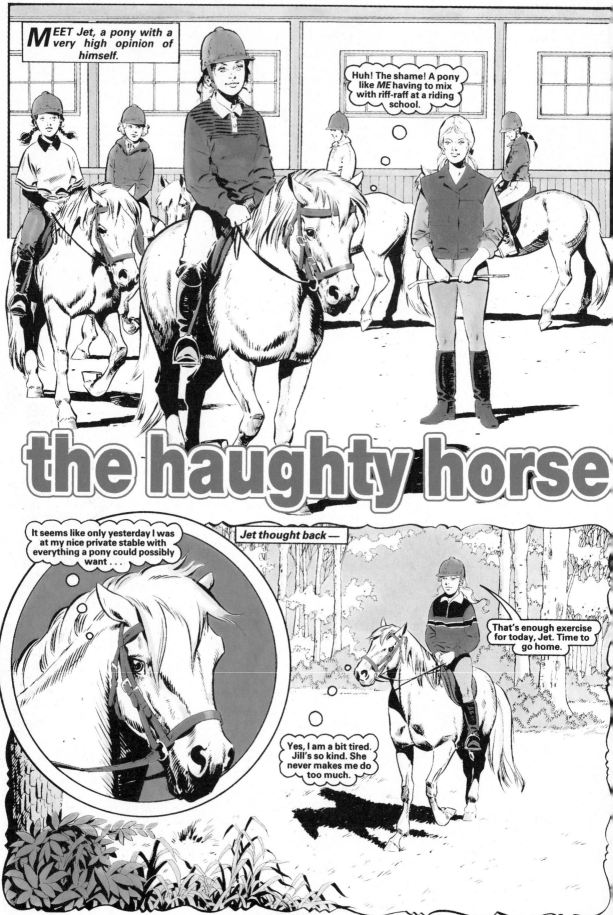

the haughty horse

Make sure my pony's well fed and watered, Susan.

Yes, miss.

Mmm, delicious. Susan has mixed my feed just the way I like it. It's good having my own groom.

But, then —

My business is in trouble. It means we'll have to sell the house and move.

Oh, no! That's terrible, Dad!

We'll have to make other cutbacks, too, Jill.

We can't afford to keep a pony any longer. We'll have to sell Jet.

You can't! I've had him since he was a foal!

But —

The local riding school have said they'll take Jet. That way you can still visit him when you want.

It won't be the same. I'll miss Jet so much!

So, next day —

Oh, good, we're going on a trip. I hope it's somewhere nice.

But Jet was in for a shock.

Goodbye, Jet. I promise I'll come and see you soon.

Huh? What do you mean?

81

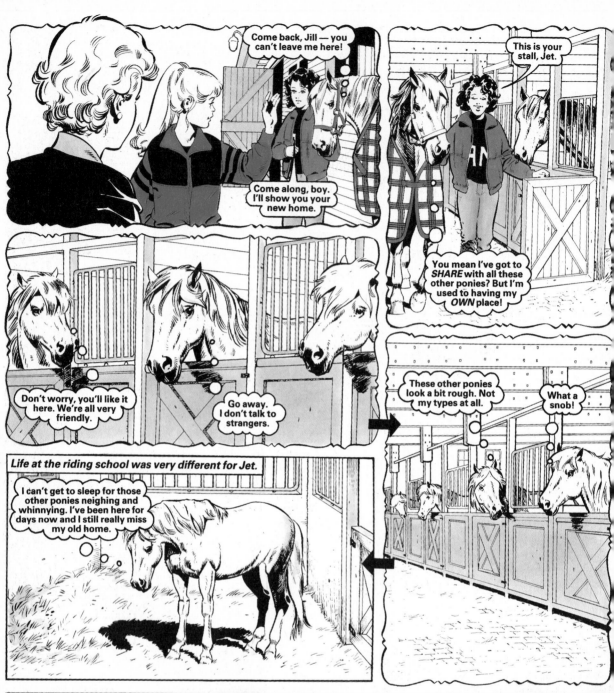

82

83

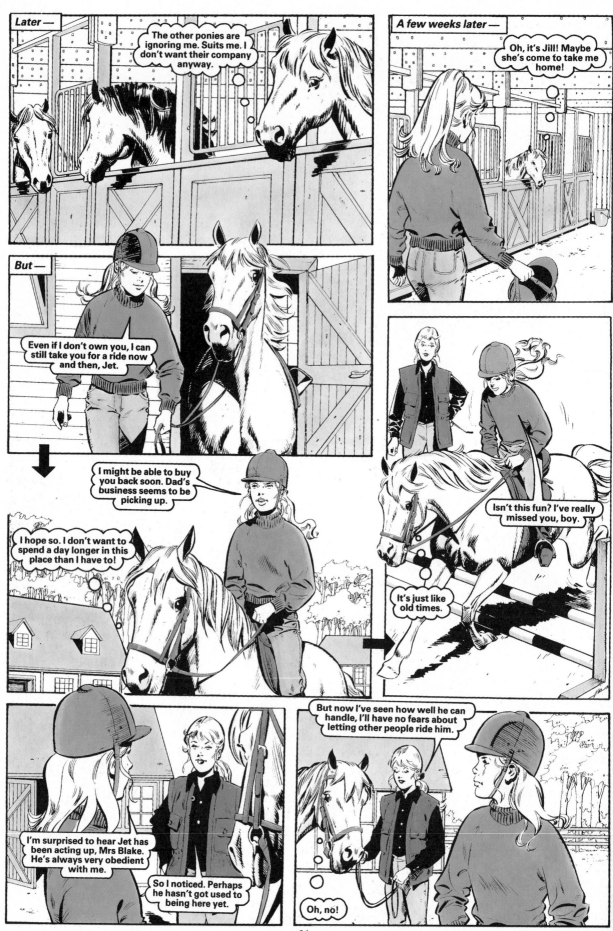

84

As the days passed, Jet didn't grow any fonder of his new life.

I don't like just being one of the crowd. When Jill owned me I was always the centre of attention.

Did you enjoy that, Karen?

Not really! This new pony's no fun to ride. He just seems dead sad.

A pony-trekking weekend? I don't fancy the sound of that . . .

Well, maybe the pony-trekking weekend will be better for you.

Yes, I'm really looking forward to it — as long as I don't get stuck with HIM. See you on Friday!

On Friday —

Everyone's here except Karen, Mrs Blake.

We can't wait any longer for her, Helen. Choose your ponies for the weekend, everyone.

We'll camp at the lake, girls. Tomorrow we'll have some competitions and then come back to the stables on Sunday.

There were seven riders and eight ponies.

Nobody wanted me. None of them likes me.

You'd better take Jet back to his stall, Helen.

At least I'll have some peace and quiet again over the weekend, without all those other ponies around.

But —

It — it's lonely here by myself. I don't want to be left behind — I want to go with the others!

Then —

Sorry I'm late, Mrs Blake. My dad's car had a flat tyre on the way here.

You're just in time, Karen. And you're in luck, too — there's still one pony in the stalls.

Oh, no! Not him. Well, I suppose he'll have to do.

Hurray! I'm going after all!

And, at the camp —

These races and games are fun. I DO like being one of the crowd! I don't even mind getting my hooves muddy!

We won!

Carrie's Choice

88

Next day —

Mum, I'm just going round to see Gran . . .

. . . and Ross, too, I hope, since he lives in the same street.

And —

Hi, Ross. Good book?

Brilliant! It's an adventure mystery . . .

Fifteen minutes later —

. . . and that's as far as I've got.

Phew! I thought Ross was never gonna stop going on about that book. He talks too MUCH!

Back at home —

Looks like it's the coin after all. I STILL can't decide, but I've GOT to go with someone — everyone else is. So who will it be?

Hang on! I can't decide which one to go with because really I don't want to go with EITHER! But if I don't take a partner I'll be the odd one out.

the end

Bon Voyage!

HANNAH'S dad stopped reading her school report and looked up. "This is very good, love," he said. "Apart from French, that is."

"I try, Dad," sighed Hannah, "but I'm hopeless. I've tried explaining to Madame Fournier that it doesn't matter because I want a job in sport when I leave school."

"And what does she say to that?" asked Mum.

"Ah, but we are in Europe now, Hannah. How would you feel if you had to turn down a great job in France because you could not speak the language?"

Mum laughed as Hannah tried to copy her teacher's accent.

"Well, she has got a point," Mum said. "But then, you can only try your best. And you do well at everything else — especially sports."

> **Hannah groaned inside. Extra homework meant she would have to miss football practice.**

"All this talk about French has reminded me of an offer in the paper," Dad said. "How would you both fancy a day out in Calais?"

"Sounds great!" cried Hannah. "When can we go?"

"Lovely," Mum agreed. "I can't wait to go shopping in France!"

The trip was arranged for the following Saturday. Hannah was really looking forward to it — though she still had double French to get through before then.

"Have you been asleep all lesson, Hannah?" asked Madame Fournier as she gazed at Hannah's unfinished work. "I'm afraid I shall just have to give you extra homework."

Hannah groaned inside. Extra homework meant she would have to miss football practice.

Saturday arrived at last and it was a relief for Hannah to be aboard the ferry and have the warm sun shining on her face. After a lovely day in Calais, her parents went shopping in the Hypermarket while Hannah sat in the sun on the sea wall.

She breathed in the fresh salty air. School and Madame Fournier seemed a million miles away.

"Bonjour."

A voice made Hannah jump. She turned her head to see a good-looking boy about her own age. He had a bright friendly smile.

"Nice day, n'est-ce pas?" said the boy. "You are English, yes? You not like le shopping? Me also. Sorry, my English not good."

"My French not good also," smiled Hannah.

"Je m'appelle Jean-Claude," said the boy. "Et vous?"

"Hannah," she replied, feeling pleased because she could understand a bit of French after all.

With a lot of gesturing and laughing the pair slowly managed to carry on a conversation.

It seemed that Jean-Claude was visiting the coast with his parents for the day. He loved football and knew the names of all the top English players. He was very impressed when Hannah told him that she was the captain of her team.

All too soon, though, Hannah's parents came hurrying out of the Hypermarket saying it was time to go for the ferry. Hannah had to say goodbye to her new friend. As the ferry bus left for the harbour, Jean-Claude waved to Hannah.

"We're going to write to each other," Hannah told her mum as they sat down to tea in the ferry restaurant. "Me in French and Jean-Claude in English, so that we can help each other."

"Good idea," smiled Mum. "Jean-Claude could be just the encouragement you need."

"Right then, here we are," said Dad, as he passed them each a yummy fresh cream chocolate eclair. "Thought we'd have a bit of a treat."

"Wow," said Hannah. "Merci beaucoup, Dad. And bon appétit!"

THE END

make my day

Meet Michelle Higgins. She fancied a make-over so how could we refuse? We whisked her off to the studio where Karen the make-up artist, Gordon the photographer and a *massive* pile of clothes waited. Check out Michelle's day.

1 Karen puts rollers in my hair first. This is so they'll set while my make-up's being done. *Help!* I look like a gran!

2 Hmm — pretty! But al supermodels wear th — or so I'm told.

3 Now for the make-up. Karen applies a natural tinted moisturiser and light dusting of powder to make my skin shine-free. Then she moves on to the eyes.

4 After using a pale bluey-lilac eyesh Karen adds mascara to finish.

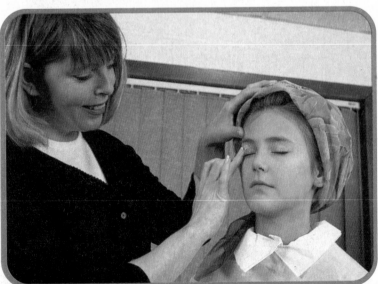

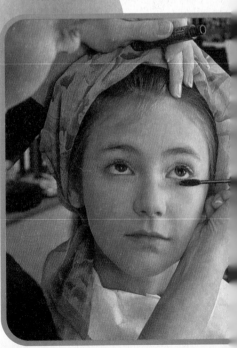

5 Rosy lip gloss completes the make-up.

6 Pale silver polish makes my nails glitter and shine.

7 At last! The rollers are out. They've added lots of bounce 'n' volume to my fine hair. Not sure about the style, though!

8 That's better! Karen gently brushes it through to create a lovely smooth style. A glittery hair clip finishes things off.

95

9 The new me! What d'you think? Nice, eh?

Turn over for more ▶

10 Hey, it didn't take *all* this to make me over, did it?

11 Now for the clothes. *Wow!* What a choice!

12 Hmm. Modelling's not all glamorous — these are the things you *don't* see in the photos.

13 Look out, Kate Moss — here I come!

14 Well, even supermodels need donuts! *Yum!*

nurses

on t.v.

CONTINUED FROM PAGE 19.

Ben has a high temperature and he's very drowsy. Has he been sick, Mrs Jackson?

Yes, Doctor.

A TELEVISION documentary about hospital life was being filmed at Norchester General Hospital, where Verity, Amanda, Jackie and Kay were student nurses. A very sick baby had just arrived in the Children's Ward where Jackie was working —

It could be meningitis, but we'll need to do some tests.

Oh, no!

Don't cry, Mrs Jackson. Ben's in good hands.

Can I call my husband? He's working in Germany. I want him to come home.

Of course. You can use the phone in my office.

Excuse me, would you mind if we filmed your baby for our TV documentary?

What? Oh — yes, go ahead.

Soon —

We've had the results of the tests on Ben Jackson. It's bacterial meningitis. He's to be treated with antibiotics, and the next couple of days will be critical.

At lunchtime —

Now, what'll we have? Some kind of pasta, I think . . .

I'm Babs — a lighting assistant with the film crew.

Of course! I recognise you now.

Then —

Hi! You're a nurse at Norchester General, aren't you?

Er — yeah — that's right.

I'm choosing something for supper.

Me, too. I'm fed up of take-aways, but I don't know what to have.

Where are you staying?

In a bed and breakfast, so there's nowhere to cook.

Why don't you come and have supper with us, then? I share with three other nurses. You can tell us all about TV life.

That'd be great — thanks!

99

That afternoon —

I'm pleased to tell you your baby is showing signs of recovery. I think he'll pull through.

Oh, good! Mr Jackson's here.

That's such a relief! Thanks very much for all you've done.

Ben should be okay, so that'll give you a happy ending to your documentary.

I'm afraid it WON'T.

What do you mean?

When Mr Jackson arrived, he withdrew permission for his baby to be filmed. We can't use the story.

Oh, no! So all your film was wasted?

I'm afraid so. It's such a pity — we did a good job.

Look, don't go just yet. Maybe I can help.

"OH YES

12-year-old Suzannah Wood has wanted to be a dancer since she was two! Now she's got her first dancing role in the pantomime, Snow White.

Suzannah auditioned with 180 other girls to be one of the 12 senior dancers. The lucky 12 rehearsed every day for a week and have to be at the stage door one hour before the panto starts.

Four nights a week, Suzannah has modern, ballet, disco and stage dancing classes. She used to do Drama, too, but couldn't fit the lessons into her busy schedule!

Eventually Suzannah would like to take up acting and go to Drama School. She loves dressing up and there are some brilliant outfits in the Wardrobe Department.

HE IS!"

Behind the scenes at a pantomime

Suzannah and the girls were thrilled when they discovered that their Saturday morning favourites — Ant and Dec — were to be the stars of the show. And lucky Suzannah got to cuddle up close to both of them for this panto pic!

Filipa Jeronimo is the Wicked Queen. She told Suzannah that it's tradition that the nasty characters enter stage left and the goodies stage right — so now you know!

And here they are — the cast of Snow White, ready for their next performance, with Suzannah on her first step to stardom (Oh yes, she is!).

103

Suspicion!

THIRTEEN-YEAR-OLD Heather Lee had lots of friends.

Eat your hearts out, gang. I've just got a new CD player.

Oh, Mum and Dad gave me one of these *AGES* ago!

Huh! What *HASN'T* Catriona got?

Hey, check this out, Catriona! Heather's little model of a deer is dead cool.

My aunt's got one like that — but it's *REAL* china. She got it when she did her coast to coast tour of America.

I suppose she can't help it, Lynne. And it must be cool getting everything you want.

105

Hey, here's Hannah.

Hi, everyone. This is my cousin, Amy. She's staying with us at weekends just now. I brought her along.

Great. Hi, Amy!

Heather went downstairs for some drinks —

Catriona goes on a bit, but she's still a good mate. It's great having so many pals.

Hey, watch it, Gemma. Why don't you and your friend play in your room?

Crisps 95

Later, after Heather had walked her friends home —

Hey, I thought I told you two to stay in GEMMA'S room!

Sorry, Heather. I was just letting Alison see your magazine.

Then, minutes later —

My little deer's gone! I don't believe this! Gemma and Alison must have moved it!

But when Heather asked them about it —

Mum! Heather says that Alison and I took her deer. But we DIDN'T. We never TOUCHED it.

I just asked her where it was, Mum. They were playing about with my stuff and now it's gone.

Yes, well I suggest you tidy your room before you accuse people, Heather. It's a tip!

Trust Mum to say that! But I suppose she's right.

106

But, later —

Did you find the deer, Heather?

No! Look, I'm sorry for upsetting you, Gemma. I know you and Alison wouldn't take my ornament. I just don't know where it's gone.

I'm glad to see you're friends again. Why not ask the girls about the missing deer, Heather? Maybe one of them will know something about it.

Okay, Mum. I will.

Next day —

Mum's right — maybe one of my friends took it home by mistake. Oh! There's Lynne. I'll go catch her up.

Then —

I don't believe I'm seeing this. She's nicking that chocolate. Maybe she nicked my deer, too!

Oh, she was only getting out her purse! That was really stupid of me! As if Lynne would nick anything. But maybe one of the others DID.

Then, at P.E. —

That's Charlotte Donovan's bag! What's HANNAH doing looking in it?

Oh! H-hi there, Heather.

Charlie said I could borrow her spare socks 'cos I forgot my own. You'd better hurry up. Old Machin's in a foul mood.

Okay! I'm just coming.

Get moving! I want this game started sometime before Christmas!

Gosh, she IS in a bad mood! I'm glad Hannah warned me. She's a good mate — like ALL my friends.

Later —

Thanks, Catriona. That's lovely.

I don't know how I could suspect my friends. It was only a stupid deer after all — hardly worth losing my mates over.

Oh, hi, Heather! I was just wondering if you and Debbie would like to come round to watch videos tonight. The olds say I can ask two mates.

Okay.

Debbie's not really part of our crowd. I don't know why Catriona wants to be friends with her.

Later —

One thing's for certain, though, Catriona never took my deer. She's already got everything.

And, later —

Tuck in, girls. You must be hungry.

Gosh, Catriona! This is brill!

I'm really sorry, Mrs Keene, but I've got to go. I arranged to meet someone at nine.

What a rude girl! Going off after I've been to all this trouble to have her here! Don't ask her back!

Tch! I quite like her. But okay, Mum.

I guess that puts paid to Debbie. Good! Lynne and Hannah are much more fun than she is.

108

On Saturday —

Can I read that when you're finished, Catriona?

Sure.

This is the greatest, when we're all together like this. And Amy's nice, too. We make a good gang.

But, later —

My ring's gone, Heather. I left it in the bathroom when I had a shower this morning and it's gone!

Oh, no! I'll bet it was AMY who took it. I saw her coming in here, and she is the new one, after all.

Heather spoke to her mum —

I'm sorry, Heather, but if that's true, then I don't want Amy back here!

This could be awkward.

At school —

Hi, Heather.

Hi, gang!

Should I tell the others my suspicions about Amy? I wouldn't like her to steal from anyone else.

Mind you, Amy's only around at weekends, so I guess I could keep an eye on her.

But —

Hey, check this one out! 'I think my best friend is a thief. Every time she comes to my house something goes missing.' Tch! Imagine being stupid enough to stay friends with a thief!

Eh? How can you talk like that when your own COUSIN'S a thief, Hannah?

Not good. They're going to operate tomorrow.

Oh, no!

I'm sorry to hear about Amy's mum, Hannah.

Yeah? I can't think why! We can do without YOUR sympathy, thank you.

I don't know what's happened between you and Hannah, Heather, but don't let her bother you.

Yeah — you've still got us.

But, then —

Wait for me, Debbie! We can be partners.

Well it looks like I've only got Catriona when Debbie Ferrant's not around. And if Lynne's the thief, then I've got NO-ONE!

After school —

I got you this for Gran's birthday party next week. The dolphin matches that bracelet she gave you.

Oh, so it does.

I'd better look out the bracelet later.

But —

It's GONE! Oh, no! It cost Gran a fortune, I've GOT to get it back!

What are you doing, Heather?

Setting a trap, Gemma.

If I leave this ring lying here Lynne's sure to take it. Then I'll know for sure that she's the thief and I can demand my bracelet back.

A little later —

POP-TASTIC!

Are you pop mad — or is your knowledge just bad?
Check out our puzzles and see how you score.

GO SQUARE!

Solve the clues and see if you can fit the answers correctly into the grid. We've given you a few letters to start you off.

1. Does this entertainer look at LIFE THRU A LENS? (6, 8)

2. This young American girlie reached No 1 with her first British single ONE MORE TIME. (7, 6)

3. You can see them in their movie SPICE WORLD. (5, 5)

4. They'll NEVER EVER go UNDER THE BRIDGE. (3, 6)

5. Get jiggy with this man in black. (4, 5)

6. Their manager is Ronan Keating. (8)

7. Mel ALL SAINTS' baby girl. (8)

8. This B*WITCHED girlie lived in Greece. (7)

9. – – – – – – Paul Piper. (6)

10. Mel C's Spice name. (6)

11. ANOTHER – – – – –. (5)

12. Is 5, 6, 7, 8 BETTER BEST FORGOTTEN? (5)

13. This DJ had big hits with ENCORE UNE FOIS and MOVE MANIA. (4)

14. Baby Spice. (4)

15. Not Claire or Faye STEPS. (4)

16. Do they come after four? (4)

17. Lead singer with 911. (3)

18. – – – BOY SLIM. (3)

19. Not Scott, J, Sean or Rich. (3)

(Grid with starting letters: R, B, A, S)

GET CROSS!

Cross out the letters that appear 3 times or more in each box to reveal 2 fab bands from Ireland.

B	W	Z	P	B
M	D	E	D	M
S	P	B	M	T
D	Z	L	I	D
M	F	P	Z	E

T	K	W	H	A
A	E	Y	K	F
Y	F	C	K	O
W	R	R	K	Y
Y	F	A	S	W

UP 2 U!

Oooh — which is the right choice — it's up to you!

What was the title of *ROBBIE WILLIAMS'* 2nd album?

I WASN'T EXPECTING
VISITORS
COME FOR TEA
c) I'VE BEEN
   EXPECTING YOU

2. Who had a hit with HONEY TO THE BEE?
a) BILLIE
b) BRITNEY SPEARS
c) CHER

3. Which two members of ALL SAINTS are sisters?
a) NIC & NAT
b) NIC & MEL
c) MEL & NAT

4. Who are Claire, Lisa, Faye, H and Richie?
a) TAKE 5
b) WESTLIFE
c) STEPS

5. Who is PHOENIX CHI connected to?
a) MEL BLATT
b) MEL G
c) MEL C

6. Which band had a big hit with ALL THAT MATTERS?
a) BOYZONE
b) ANOTHER LEVEL
c) FIVE

7. Mel C duetted with a rocker blokie. The song was a massive hit. Who was it?
a) JON BON JOVI
b) BRUCE
   SPRINGSTEEN
c) BRYAN ADAMS

8. Which cool DJ's real name is Norman?
a) SASH!
b) FAT BOY SLIM
c) JUDGE JULES

9. ANT AND DEC used to be known by which stage names?
a) PJ & DUNCAN
b) PYJAMAS & SHORTS
c) DUNCAN & DEREK

10. Which is the longest running pop show on TV?
a) TOP TEN FLOPS
b) TOP OF THE FLOPS
c) TOP OF THE POPS

WHO AM I?

Solve the clues and guess the identity of the stars.

1. I had my first hit singles in the 60s when I was part of a duo. I have acted in lots of films including MERMAIDS and MOONSTRUCK. I like to wear wigs. I look young for my age and I had a huge No 1 hit in 1998.

2. There are five of us in the band. We come from Ireland. We've had heaps of hits. One of us manages another group and has presented a TV talent show. Two of us got married in 1998. One of us has famous twin sisters.

3. We are a foursome. We are all girls. Two of us have a famous brother. We entered the record books when our first four singles all went straight into the charts at No 1. Our first single had a French title.

4. I have had many, many hits. I have also acted in some films and was once married to an actor. I have changed my image lots of times. I have a little girl called Lourdes.

5. There are five of us and we are American. We come from Florida. One of us once modelled for Versace. The youngest member of the group has a little brother who's also a pop star. A couple of years ago, one of us had to have heart surgery.

WORDS, WORDS, WORDS!

See how many words of 3 letters or more you can make from

CHART TOPPER

15-20: GOOD 21-30: VERY GOOD More than 30: EXCELLENT

SOAP ST

We know all about our fave b
— now find out more ab

Philip Oliv
(Tinhead, Brooksi

* His fave footie team is Liverpoo
* When it comes to eating out, Philip alw
chooses Chin
* Thinks girls shouldn't wait t
asked out — THEY sh
do the ask

Daniel MacPherson
(Joel, Neighbours)

* Like his on-screen character, Joel,
Daniel is athletics mad.
* After acting, all his time is taken up
with training for triathlons.
* There's no time for girlfriends in real
life, but there's plenty
in Ramsay Street!

Jesse Spence
(Bill, Neighbours

* Erinsborough's golde
guy gets tons of fan
mail from all over th
world, and tries to
answer it all.
* He calls his car
Moses and the numbe
plate is LUC (Luck!)
* Jesse's composed
some classical musi
and wants to perform
it in public.

Graeme Squires
(Tom, Home and Away)

* First appeared as Tom Nash in November 3, 1997.
* Joined an acting class at 15 to overcome shyness.
* Lives in a remote beach house, south of Sydney, with his
pet dog, Alex, a Rhodesian Ridgeback/Rottweiler cross.

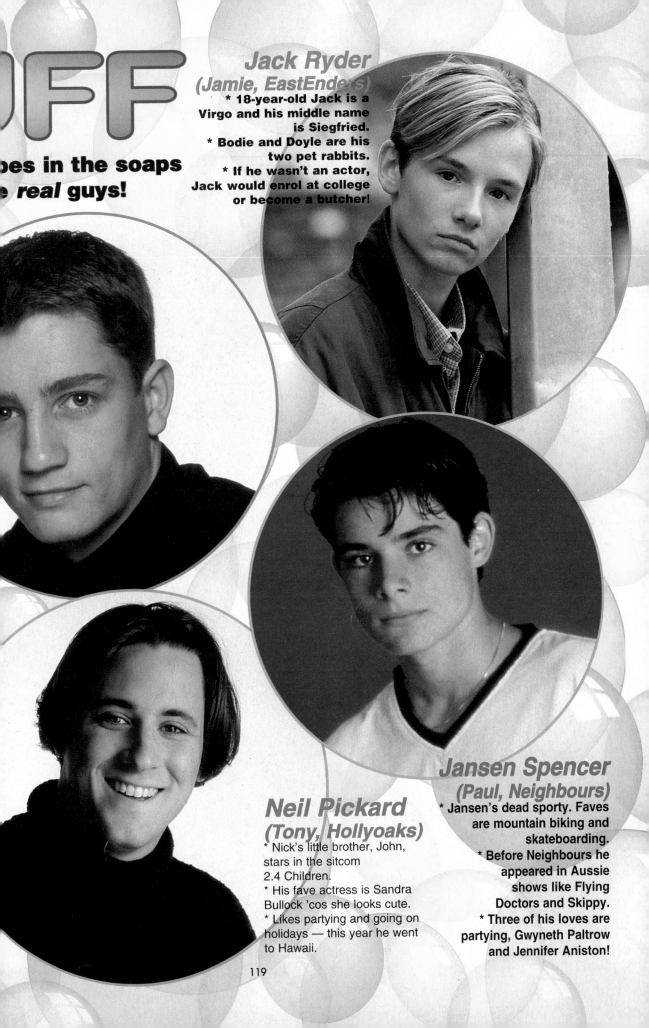

UFF

...bes in the soaps
...e *real guys!*

Jack Ryder
(Jamie, EastEnders)
* 18-year-old Jack is a Virgo and his middle name is Siegfried.
* Bodie and Doyle are his two pet rabbits.
* If he wasn't an actor, Jack would enrol at college or become a butcher!

Jansen Spencer
(Paul, Neighbours)
* Jansen's dead sporty. Faves are mountain biking and skateboarding.
* Before Neighbours he appeared in Aussie shows like Flying Doctors and Skippy.
* Three of his loves are partying, Gwyneth Paltrow and Jennifer Aniston!

Neil Pickard
(Tony, Hollyoaks)
* Nick's little brother, John, stars in the sitcom 2.4 Children.
* His fave actress is Sandra Bullock 'cos she looks cute.
* Likes partying and going on holidays — this year he went to Hawaii.

119

Only another seven days to go! But I want to open my pressies *NOW!*

IT wasn't long till Christmas — and Kelly Barton was counting the days.

HiDE AND SEEK

Brill! There's Auntie Sue with more pressies. When she's gone I'll go down and guess what *SHE'S* brought me!

But —

Er — where did you put the pressies, Mum?

Far away from *YOU*, Kelly. And if you go snooping, you might not get *ANY*.

A few days later—

I've *GOT* to have a look at my pressies soon! I'm desperate to know if Gran's got me that spangly top.

123

A Room For HAYLEY

Join Hayley in her search for the perfect room.

Hayley Flowers is about to move up from junior school to senior school and needs a bedroom where she'll be able to study and relax.

A fold-out chair, which doubles as a guest bed, is perfect for a quiet read.

"But where will all my cuddly toys go?" asks Hayley. Angela suggests more shelves for Teddy and co.

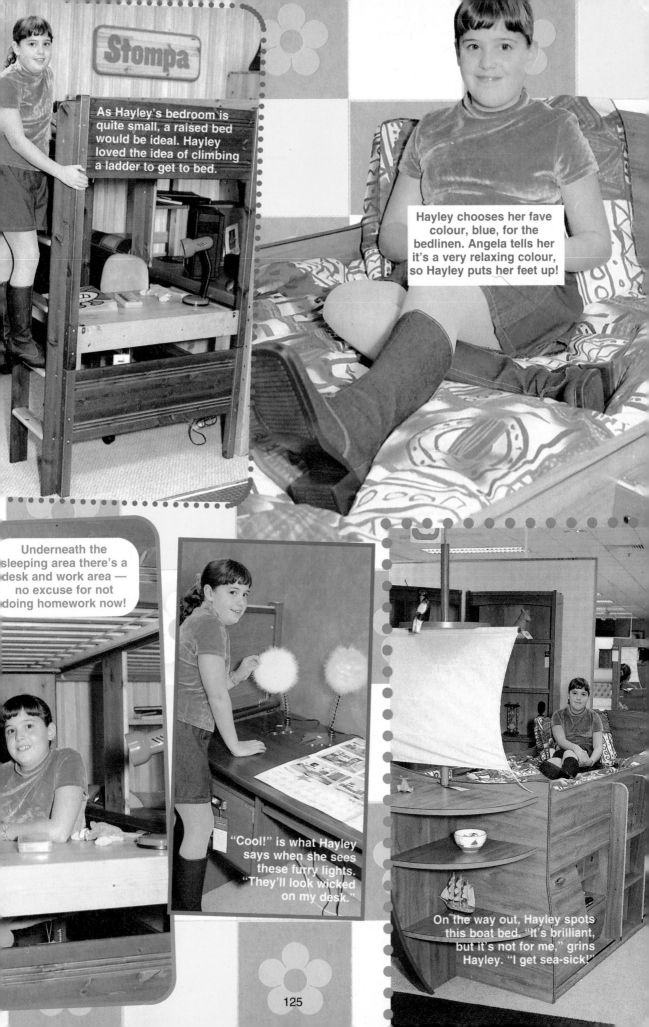

Stompa

As Hayley's bedroom is quite small, a raised bed would be ideal. Hayley loved the idea of climbing a ladder to get to bed.

Hayley chooses her fave colour, blue, for the bedlinen. Angela tells her it's a very relaxing colour, so Hayley puts her feet up!

Underneath the sleeping area there's a desk and work area — no excuse for not doing homework now!

"Cool!" is what Hayley says when she sees these furry lights. "They'll look wicked on my desk."

On the way out, Hayley spots this boat bed. "It's brilliant, but it's not for me," grins Hayley. "I get sea-sick!"

Wildlife

JULY						
S	—	2	9	16	23	30
M	—	3	10	17	24	31
T	—	4	11	18	25	—
W	—	5	12	19	26	—
T	—	6	13	20	27	—
F	—	7	14	21	28	—
S	1	8	15	22	29	—

AUGUST						
S	—	6	13	20	27	
M	—	7	14	21	28	
T	1	8	15	22	29	
W	2	9	16	23	30	
T	3	10	17	24	31	
F	4	11	18	25	—	
S	5	12	19	26	—	

SEPTEMBER						
S	—	3	10	17	24	
M	—	4	11	18	25	
T	—	5	12	19	26	
W	—	6	13	20	27	
T	—	7	14	21	28	
F	1	8	15	22	29	
S	2	9	16	23	30	